LEVEL 3

CHRISTMAS DUETS

Arranged by Jane Smisor Bastien

Preface

CHRISTMAS DUETS is designed to correlate with **Level 3** of **THE BASTIEN PIANO LIBRARY**. However, this volume may be used as supplementary enrichment with any piano course. Texts are printed apart from the music to allow space for writing in the counts. The Duets may be used for lesson material and/or for a Christmas recital.

Contents

ISBN 0-8497-6115-8

Jingle bells! Jingle bells! Jingle all the way!
Oh what fun it is to ride in a one-horse open sleigh!
Jingle bells! Jingle bells! Jingle all the way!
Oh what fun it is to ride in a one-horse open sleigh!

Jingle Bells
Secondo

James Pierpont

Jingle bells! Jingle bells! Jingle all the way!
Oh what fun it is to ride in a one-horse open sleigh!
Jingle bells! Jingle bells! Jingle all the way!
Oh what fun it is to ride in a one-horse open sleigh!

Jingle Bells
Primo

James Pierpont

Lively

GP313

O come, little children, o come, one and all!
To Bethlehem come, to the manger so small!
With stars watching o'er in a manger of hay,
God's Son has been sent on this glorious day!

O Come, Little Children
Secondo

James Bastien

J.A.P. Schulz

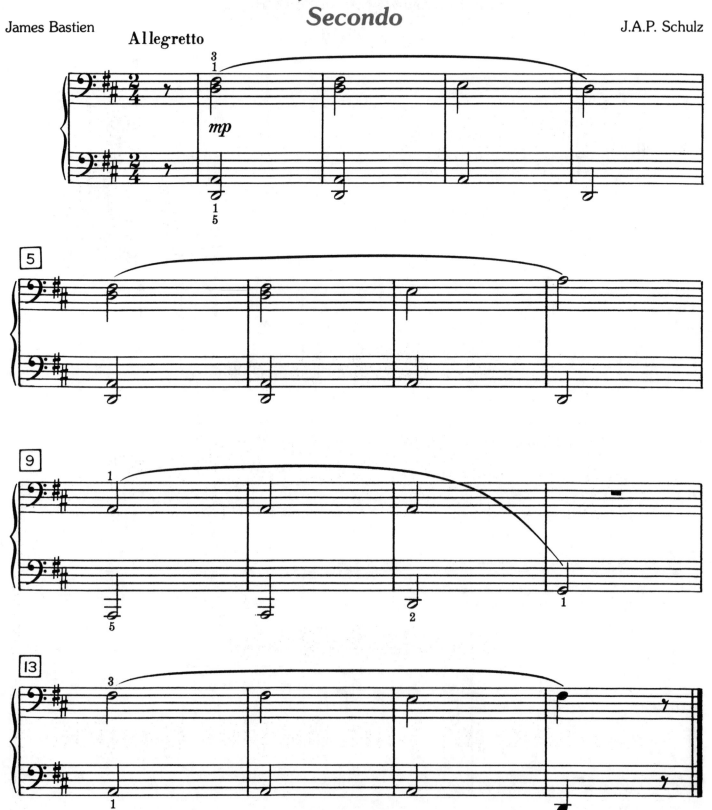

O come, little children, o come, one and all!
To Bethlehem come, to the manger so small!
With stars watching o'er in a manger of hay,
God's Son has been sent on this glorious day!

O Come, Little Children
Primo

James Bastien

J.A.P. Schulz

Silent night, holy night,
All is calm, all is bright,
'Round yon virgin Mother and Child,
Holy Infant, so tender and mild,
Sleep in heavenly peace,
Sleep in heavenly peace.

Silent Night
Secondo

Joseph Mohr

Franz Gruber

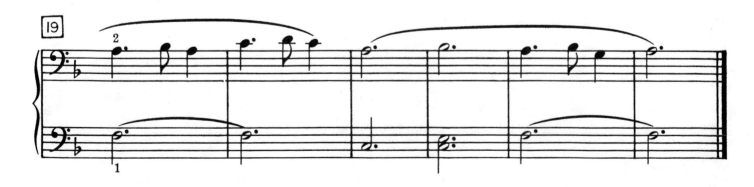

Silent night, holy night,
All is calm, all is bright,
'Round yon virgin Mother and Child,
Holy Infant, so tender and mild,
Sleep in heavenly peace,
Sleep in heavenly peace.

Silent Night
Primo

Joseph Mohr

Franz Gruber

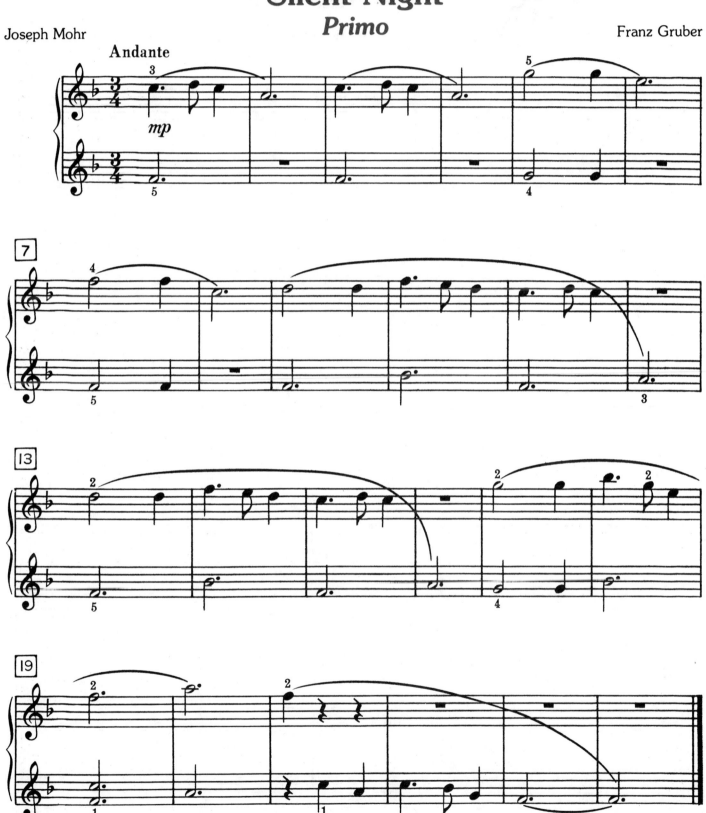

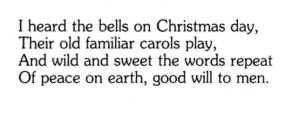

I heard the bells on Christmas day,
Their old familiar carols play,
And wild and sweet the words repeat
Of peace on earth, good will to men.

I Heard the Bells on Christmas Day
Secondo

Henry W. Longfellow

J. Baptiste Calkin

Moderato

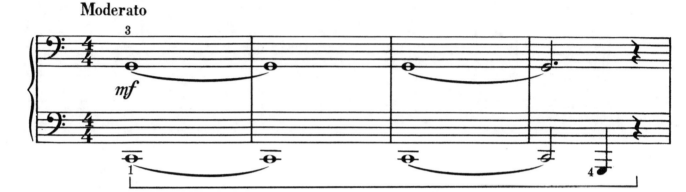

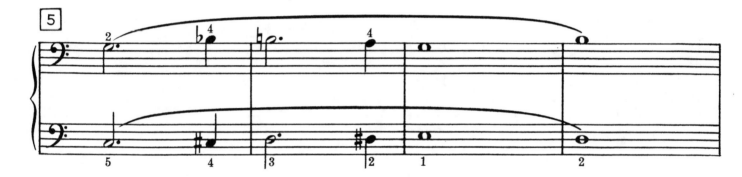

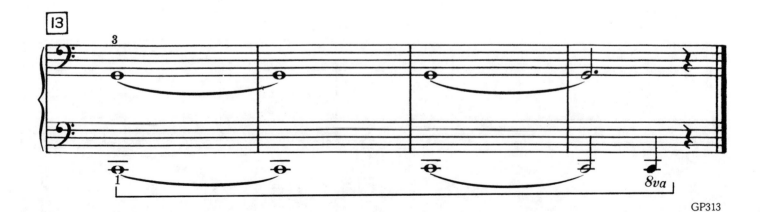

GP313

The Nativity Song

Tenderly ♩ = 100–108

1. This is the sea-son be-loved of the year.
2. This is the new star, shin-ing so bright,
3. This is the sta-ble, shel-ter so bare;

Sing a rhyme; Christ - mas - time soon will be here.
Light - ing the world on that first Christ - mas night.
Cat - tle and ox - en first wel - comed him there.

Tell the true sto - ry of Je - sus' birth,
This is the an - gel pro - claim - ing the birth,
This is the man - ger, sweet hay for a bed,

When, as a ba - by, he came to the earth.
Sing - ing "Ho - san - na!" and "Peace on the earth!"
Wait - ing for Je - sus to cra - dle his head.

4. These are the shepherds, humble and mild,
   Hast'ning to worship the heavenly child.
   These are the wise men who followed the star,
   Frankincense, gold, and myrrh brought from afar.

5. See the sweet mother, Mary so fair,
   Joseph, who guided the donkey with care.
   See the dear baby of Bethlehem,
   Little Lord Jesus, the Savior of men.

Luke 2:1–16
Matthew 2:1–11

Pictures or figures for each verse may be put in place during the four-measure introduction.

Words and music: Patricia Kelsey Graham, b. 1940. © 1980 LDS

I heard the bells on Christmas day,
Their old familiar carols play,
And wild and sweet the words repeat
Of peace on earth, good will to men.

I Heard the Bells on Christmas Day

Primo

Henry W. Longfellow

J. Baptiste Calkin

We wish you a Merry Christmas,
We wish you a Merry Christmas,
We wish you a Merry Christmas,
And a Happy New Year!
Good tidings we bring to you and your kin,
Good tidings for Christmas,
And a Happy New Year!

We Wish You a Merry Christmas
Secondo

With spirit

Traditional English Carol

We wish you a Merry Christmas,
We wish you a Merry Christmas,
We wish you a Merry Christmas,
And a Happy New Year!
Good tidings we bring to you and your kin,
Good tidings for Christmas,
And a Happy New Year!

We Wish You a Merry Christmas

Primo

Traditional English Carol

We three kings of Orient are;
Bearing gifts, we traverse afar
Field and fountain, moor and mountain,
Following yonder star.
O——— Star of wonder, Star of night,
Star with royal beauty bright,
Westward leading, still proceeding,
Guide us to the perfect light.

We Three Kings of Orient Are

Secondo

John H. Hopkins

We three kings of Orient are;
Bearing gifts, we traverse afar
Field and fountain, moor and mountain,
Following yonder star.
O——— Star of wonder, Star of night,
Star with royal beauty bright,
Westward leading, still proceeding,
Guide us to the perfect light.

We Three Kings of Orient Are

Primo

John H. Hopkins

What Child is this, Who, laid to rest
On Mary's lap, is sleeping?
Whom angels greet with anthems sweet,
While shepherds watch are keeping?
This, this is Christ the King
Whom shepherds guard and angels sing;
Haste, haste to bring Him laud,
The Babe, the Son of Mary!

What Child Is This?
Secondo

17th Century English Tune

GP313

What Child is this, Who, laid to rest
On Mary's lap, is sleeping?
Whom angels greet with anthems sweet,
While shepherds watch are keeping?
This, this is Christ the King
Whom shepherds guard and angels sing;
Haste, haste to bring Him laud,
The Babe, the Son of Mary!

What Child Is This?
Primo

17th Century English Tune

GP313